This igloo annual belongs to:

Chloe Cracknell

2012 ANNUAL

igloo

Meet **Humf**

Humf is a furry thing!

- My best friends are Loon and Wallace.
- The food I like most is spaghetti.
- My best book is 'The Little Green Bus'.
- When I grow up, I would like to be a bus, so I could take people places like the Little Green Bus does.
- I like going to the park with my friends.
- I live in Flat 2, in the middle of our building.
- My birthday is February 11th.

Playtime Fun

Humf is a ball of furry fun.
He is three years old. He likes to
play with his toy farmyard and toy animals.

Decorate Humf

Decorate this picture of
Humf playing with his toys,
using your best pens.

Humf's Friends

One day, Humf's dad was looking at a newspaper.
"Can I play with a friend today?" asked Humf.
Humf's dad took Humf up the stairs to find Wallace.

Humf rang the bell. But he didn't hear Wallace.
"I don't think Wallace is home today," said Dad. So Dad
took Humf down the stairs to find Loon.

Humf rang the bell. But he didn't hear Loon either.
"I don't think Loon is home today," said Dad.
"Maybe my friends went to the park," said Humf.

Humf looked all around the park for his friends.
But Humf couldn't find Wallace and Loon anywhere.
"I don't have any friends to play with!" said Humf.

"What about me?" asked Dad.
"Silly Dad," said Humf. "You're not a friend. You're a DAD!"
"But I like to play, too," said Dad.

So, Humf's dad swung on the swings with Humf.
He also climbed on the climbing frame with Humf.
But he was too big to slide down the slide!

So they played in the sandpit instead.
Humf's dad made the best sandcastle ever.
Then Wallace and Loon came to the park with Loon's mum.

Now Humf had lots of friends to play with.
Wallace and Loon and Humf and Humf's dad made
sandcastles together all afternoon.

Look Closely

Can you match the close-up pieces to the pictures?

Answers on page 65

Spot the Difference

Answers on page 65

Can you spot the five differences between these two pictures?

a

b

9

Loon's Finger Flutterbies

You will need:
- A pencil
- A piece of card
- A Paintbrush
- Paints

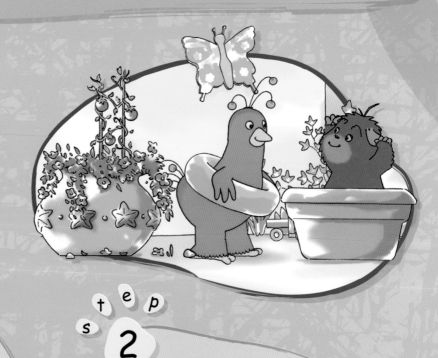

step 1
Using the pencil, draw a shape of a butterfly onto the card.

step 2
Paint your butterfly. Remember to make the body a different color to the wings.

step 3
Paint the tips of your fingers and use your fingerprints to decorate your butterfly's wings, as shown in the picture below. Remember, your thumbs will make bigger prints than your fingers.

step 4
Try making lots of different butterflies in all sorts of shapes and sizes. You can use your fingerprints to make different patterns on each one, as shown in the pictures below!

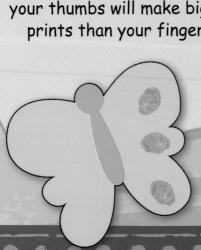

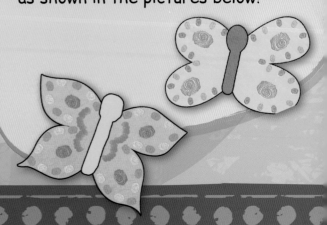

Let's Make a Boat

step 1

Roll the sticky tack into a ball. Stick it to the bottom of the container, in the middle, as shown in the picture below.

You will need:
- A straw
- Sticky tack
- A piece of card
- A plastic container
- Poster paints
- A Paintbrush
- Sticky tape
- PVA glue
- Pens

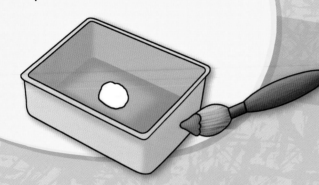

step 2

Mix four parts paint to one part PVA glue and paint the container.

step 3

Ask an adult to cut a triangle from the piece of card. Decorate it using your pens and stick it to the top of the straw using the tape. This will be your sail.

step 4

Push the long end of the straw into the sticky tack, as shown in the picture below. This will hold the sail in place. Now you're ready to sail your boat!

Meet
Loon

Loon is a feathery thing!

- My best friends are Humf and Wallace.

- I like dancing and ballet.

- I like digging for treasure, like a pirate.

- I don't like yucky things!

- The toy I like most is my magic wand. It doesn't do real magic though!

- My best hat is a tiara. It's a kind of crown.

- I live in Flat 1, at the bottom of our building.

- My birthday is October 28th.

Decorate Loon

Loon can fly, but only a little bit.
She is Humf's best friend, along with Wallace.
Loon likes to talk a lot and explain things.

Dot to Dot

Join the dots together to reveal Loon. Then use your best pencils to decorate the picture.

Humf's Special Cup

Uncle Hairy had a new job and a new briefcase with lots of pockets. There was even a bottle of water inside. "That's in case I get thirsty at work," said Uncle Hairy.

"I have a special cup," said Humf. He'd had it since he was a very small furry thing. Even though Humf was big now, he still liked his special cup.

At dinner time, Mum and Dad couldn't find Humf's special cup anywhere. They looked in his bed and in his toy box, in the bathtub and the sink and even in the plant pots.

Humf looked under the sofa and behind the cushions, too, but his special cup wasn't there either. "Never mind," said Dad. "You can use a big cup tonight."

Humf drank slowly and carefully from the big cup. Then Uncle Hairy came back and Humf put the big cup down, but his big fork was in the way. "Oops!" said Humf.

"Never mind," said Uncle Hairy. "Everybody has accidents, even when they're big." Mum poured some more juice and this time Humf didn't spill a drop.

"I guess you won't be needing this anymore," said Uncle Hairy opening his briefcase and bringing out Humf's special cup. "It was inside my briefcase."

"Can I have my juice in my special cup, please?" asked Humf. Humf liked Uncle Hairy a lot. He also liked his special cup — even though he was very big!

Spot the Odd One Out

Can you spot which of these pictures is the odd one out?
What is different about it?

a

b

c

Which Way?

Which line should Humf
follow to find his toy?

Answers
on page 65

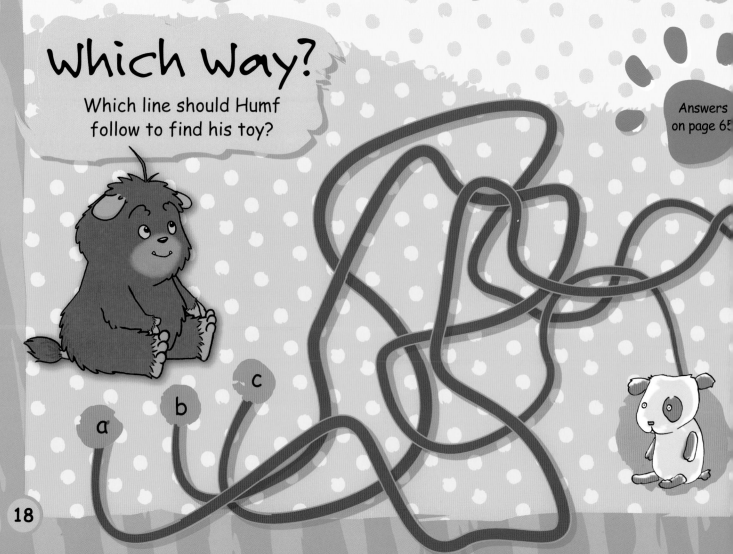

a

b

c

Picture Puzzle

Can you spot the two pieces that complete the picture?

a.

b.

c.

d.

Match the Shadow

Can you spot which shadow matches the picture of Loon?

a

c

Answers on page 65

d

b

19

Make a Shaker

You will need:
- Dried rice
- Poster paint
- A paintbrush
- 2 plastic bottles with caps
- PVA glue
- A funnel

step 1

Wash the inside of the plastic bottles and take off any labels from the outside.

step 2

Ask an adult to help you pour the rice into the bottles using the funnel until it is a quarter full, as shown in the picture on the right. Then screw the cap onto the bottle.

step 3

Ask an adult to mix four parts paint with one part PVA glue and then paint the outside of both bottles and leave them to dry.

step 4

Paint some swirls and dots onto the bottles, as shown in the pictures on the right. Leave them to dry. Then get shaking!

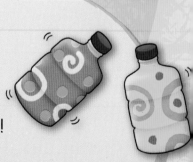

Make a Card

step 1

Fold the blue card in half. Ask an adult to cut a circle from the yellow card. Draw a face on it with your pens and stick this to the front of your blue card, as shown in the picture on the right.

You will need:
• Stick glue
• A piece of yellow card
• A piece of blue card
• Glitter
• Pens

step 2

Using the stick glue, draw wavy lines around the circle, for sun beams.

step 3

Put newspaper down and place your card on top. Sprinkle the glitter over the glue. Tap the card so that the extra glitter falls onto the newspaper.

step 4

When your card has dried, use your best pens to write a message inside the card.

Hop, Skip and Away

You will need a friend to play along with you. Each of you will need to use a coin for a counter. You will also need a die.

Start

1 2 3

12 11 10

13 14 15

24 23 22

25 26 27

How To Play

1. Put your coins on the start space.

2. Take turns to roll the die.

3. If you land on a space with a picture of Humf, move forward three spaces. If you land on a space with a picture of Loon, move back two spaces.

4. The first one to reach the finish square wins!

Egg Heads

You will need:
- Paint
- Cress seeds
- A paintbrush
- A cotton wool ball
- A boiled egg
- An egg cup
- A spoon

step 1

Place your egg in the egg cup and break the top off using a spoon.

step 2

Scoop out your egg. As an adult to help you wash out the shell. Using the paint and the paintbrush, paint a smiley face on the front of your egg, as shown in the picture on the right.

step 3

Run the cotton wool ball under cold water and squeeze it out, it should be damp but not soaking wet. Place this in your egg.

step 4

Sprinkle your cress seeds on the damp cotton wool ball. It will take a few days before your seeds begin to grow and create cress hair, as shown in the picture on the right. Remember to keep the cotton wool damp.

Potato Stamping

You will need:
- Paper
- A saucer
- A paintbrush
- A sharp knife
- Potatoes
- Paint
- A pen

step 1

Wash the potato and ask an adult to cut it in half. On the flat side of the potato, use your pen to draw the shape you would like.

step 2

Ask an adult to cut around it, about one cm below the rim of the potato, using the knife.

step 3

Pour some paint into a saucer and dab the potato stamp in the paint, as shown in the picture below. Stamp your shapes onto the piece of paper.

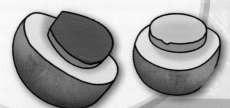

step 4

Try making pictures with your shapes. You can use your paintbrush to finish off your pictures, too, as shown in the picture below.

Meet
Wallace

Wallace is a hairy thing!

- My best friends are Humf and Loon.

- I like jumping and running and being fast.

- The television show I like the most is called 'Super Tiger'. Super Tiger is very fast.

- When I grow up, I want to be a fireman, so I can put out fires with a hose.

- I like books about dinosaurs, because they say "Roooarrr!"

- I live in Flat 3, at the top of our building.

- My birthday is April 5th.

Drawing Fun

Wallace is full of energy and bounces and runs very fast when he plays with Humf and Loon.

Decorate Wallace

Using your best pens, have fun completing and decorating the picture of Wallace.

Humf's New Word

Dad was working on the computer. "Can you read me a story?" asked Humf. "Actually, I'm a little busy right now," said Dad. So Humf went to find Mum.

"Can you read me a story?" asked Humf.
"Actually, I need to go to the supermarket," said Mum.
"What does *actually* mean?" asked Humf.

3

"It means *really*," said Mum. "You might say,
Actually, I want to go to the park."
"Actually, I do want to go to the park," said Humf.

4

Humf liked his new word. He tried using it at the
supermarket. "Can I push the trolley, actually?" he asked.
"Actually, can we get this cereal please, Mum?"

Humf tried using his new word on the way home, too.
"Mum, can we actually go to the park now?" he asked.
"Okay," said Mum. "Perhaps your friends will be there, too?"

Humf tried using his new word in the park, too.
"Actually, I think I have sand in my fur!" said Humf.
"Me too, actually!" said Wallace.

7

In fact, Humf tried using his new word everywhere! When it was time for him to go in the bathtub he asked, "Can I put my boats in the bath, actually?"

8

"Goodnight, actually," said Humf, when it was time to go to bed. Humf liked his new word. He wondered if he'd learn another new word tomorrow... actually.

How Tall Are You?

You will need:
- Scissors
- Sticky tape
- Tape Measure
- 3 sheets of green paper
- 2 sheets of yellow paper
- 1 metre (3ft 3in) of brown paper
- Stick glue
- A Pen

step 1

Ask an adult to cut out the shape of a tree trunk, 1 metre (3 ft 3 in) tall, using the brown paper. Using green paper, cut out some small and large leaf shapes

step 2

Stick the large leaves to the top of the tree trunk, using the stick glue. Cut strips 2.5cm (1 in) wide from the yellow paper and stick them to the centre of the trunk, to make a long strip.

step 3

Using the tape measure, plot the measurements onto the yellow strip, as shown in the picture below. Stick the finished height chart to the wall using sticky tack.

step 4

Every time you measure your height, write the date on one of the small leaves and stick it at the height you are measured at, as shown in the picture on the right.

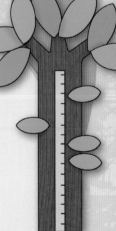

Blowing Bubbles

Use a plastic cup for the bubble solution, as shown in the picture on the right. Ask an adult to help mix nine parts of water with one part washing up liquid.

You will need:
- A pipe cleaner
- A plastic cup
- Washing up liquid
- Water

step 2

Bend one end of the pipe cleaner to form the shape of a circle.

step 3

Close the circle by wrapping the end around the stem of the pipe cleaner, as shown in the picture below.

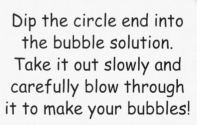

step 4

Dip the circle end into the bubble solution. Take it out slowly and carefully blow through it to make your bubbles!

Mum

Mum loves to talk on the telephone.

- I love reading stories to Humf. He likes to hear the same story, again and again and again!

- I like painting, drawing and making pretty pictures.

- I also like having parties and dancing.

- I like watching soap operas on television.

- I once had a job driving a bus.

- I love to go outside when it snows.

Playtime in the Park

Mum loves going to the park with Humf.
They have lots of fun playing on
the swings.

Complete the Scene

Complete the scene by drawing
Mum and Humf having fun at the
park. Try to draw Mum pushing
Humf on the swing.

Make Humf's Den

You will need:
- Clean linen, such as: bed sheets, blankets and tablecloths
- Clothes pegs
- Cushions
- Games

step 1

Clear a space in a room. Place some chairs around the edge of the space. This will be the inside of your den.

step 2

Ask an adult to find some old sheets, blankets, or tablecloths and drape them between sofas and chairs, tying the ends to cupboard and door handles. You can use clothes pegs to help keep them in place, as shown in the picture on the right.

step 3

Place some cushions and a blanket on the floor inside the den. Fill the inside with activities, such as games, jigsaws and books.

step 4

Find some special snacks and have a picnic inside your den. You could even give it a name and make a sign using cardboard and your best pens!

Make a Party Hat

step

1

Fold out the cereal box flat. Place a dinner plate, upside down, over the cereal box. Draw round the outline of the plate. Using a ruler, draw a line down the middle of the circle, as shown in the picture on the right.

You will need:
- A pen
- Elastic
- Sticky tape
- Tissue paper
- An empty cereal box
- A dinner plate
- A paintbrush
- A ruler
- Scissors
- Paint

step

2

Ask an adult to cut out the round shape and cut along the line, so you end up with two semi circles. Use the paint to decorate them. Tear the tissue paper into thin strips.

step

3

Curl the semi circles into a cone shape. Where the ends meet, stick them together using sticky tape, as shown in the picture on the right.

step

4

Ask an adult to pierce two holes on either side of the hats, at the bottom. Tie the elastic through one hole and put the hat on. Ask an adult to tie the other end in place. Tape the tissue paper strips to the top of the hat, as shown in the picture on the right.

Humf's Ball

One day, Uncle Hairy came to visit.
"I've brought you a present, Humf," Said Hairy.
"I like presents!" said Humf.

Uncle Hairy gave Humf a big, round, yellow thing.
"What is it?" asked Humf.
"It's a big bouncy ball," said Uncle Hairy.

Humf's new ball was very, very bouncy!
He bounced it in the sitting room and in the bedroom and in
Mum's mop bucket. SPLASH! "Oops!" said Uncle Hairy.

So, Humf and Uncle Hairy took Humf's bouncy ball to the
park. Wallace was in the park, too. Wallace tried to
see how high Humf's ball could bounce.

But Humf's ball got stuck in a tree!
"I have to go home now," said Wallace. "Bye."
Humf wasn't tall enough to get his ball down by himself.

So Humf had to use a big stick to get it down.
SHHHHH... the ball started whispering. "It must have a
hole," said Humf. Then his flat ball fell out of the tree.

Humf and Uncle Hairy took Humf's flat ball home.
Uncle Hairy put a plaster over the hole.
Then he blew it up into a big, round ball again.

"I don't think my ball wants to bounce anymore," said Humf.
So he took it to his room and read it his best story instead,
the one about the Little Green Bus.

Race to the Park

Start

1

2

3
Stop to play
in the trees.
Miss a turn.

4

5

6

7
Jump in
the puddles.
Jump forward
one space.

8

9

10

11

12

42

How To Play

You will need a friend to play along with you.
Each of you will need to use a coin for a counter.
You will also need a die.

1. Put your coins on the start space.
Take turns to roll the die.

2. Follow the instructions on the spaces
where you land.

3. The first person to reach
the finish, wins!

22
Stop to play
in the leaves.
Miss a turn.

21

13
Put some
litter in the
bin. Move
forward two
spaces.

20

23

19

14

24

18

Finish

17
Stop to smell the
flowers. Move back
a space.

Make a Sock Puppet

You will need:
- 2 buttons
- An old sock
- A sheet of brown paper
- A sheet of pink paper
- A pair of scissors
- Glue

step 1

Ask an adult to help you cut out the shape of a tongue from the pink paper. Put a sock on your hand. Create a mouth by tucking part of the sock between your thumb and palm. Stick the tongue with glue into the puppet's mouth.

step 2

Ask an adult to cut out two ovals, and one round shape, from the brown paper — these will be the puppet's ears and nose.

step 3

Glue an ear on either side of the puppet's head and the nose in the middle. Glue the buttons onto the sock for eyes, as shown in the picture above.

step 4

Try making different kinds of sock puppets, like a kitten puppet, as shown in the picture on the right.

Wallace's Blot Painting

step 1

Fold a piece of paper in half and then unfold it. Draw half of a butterfly shape on one side of the fold.

You will need:
- Glitter
- A paintbrush
- A sheet of white paper
- A pencil
- Paint

step 2

Decorate your drawing with paint. Fold the paper over at the central crease, before the paint dries, as shown in the picture on the right.

step 3

Unfold the paper. The other half of the paper will be blotted and you will have the full shape of a butterfly.

step 4

Leave the painting to one side to dry. Once it has dried decorate it with glitter, as shown in the picture below.

45

Dad

Dad likes to play with Humf.

- I like watching football on television.
- I also like being a tickle monster.
- I like to carry Humf on my shoulders and run around.
- I work a lot on the computer.
- Sometimes I have to go away on an aeroplane for work.
- I like to stay in bed late at the weekend.
- Uncle Hairy is my brother.

46

Let's Draw...

Dad is a furry thing, too. Dad likes to play outside and have fun with Humf.

Decorate Dad and Humf

Have fun shading in and decorating the picture of Dad and Humf. You can use your best pens and glitter, too.

Make Paper Flowers

You will need:
- A pair of scissors
- Pipe cleaners
- Tissue paper

step 1

Ask an adult to help you cut out some squares of tissue paper, approximately 10cm (4 in) by 10cm (4 in).

step 2

Place three squares of paper together and fold them backwards and forwards into a fan shape, as shown in the picture on the right.

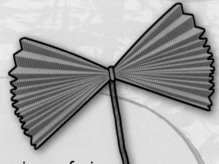

step 3

Wrap a piece of pipe cleaner around the middle of the fan and twist until it's secure, as shown in the picture above.

step 4

Carefully spread the sheets of paper out into the shape of a flower. Try using different shades of paper to create different flowers, as shown in the pictures on the right.

Make a Jigsaw

s t e p
1

Draw a picture and decorate it using your best pens and crayons. Stick your picture to a piece of card using stick glue. Leave it to dry.

You will need:
- A pair of scissors
- A sheet of card
- Stick glue
- A pencil
- Pens

s t e p
2

Ask an adult to help you cut the picture into lots of different shapes. The bigger the pieces, the easier the jigsaw will be.

s t e p
3

Mix all the pieces up and try to put them back together again. To make the jigsaw a little harder, ask an adult to cut the bigger pieces in two, or three shapes, then mix it all up and start again!

Loon's New Handbag

Loon had a new handbag. "It's for carrying my important things in," said Loon. She had a tiara, a toy helicopter and a pen that smelled like strawberries.

Humf wanted a bag, too, so he went to get his rucksack that looked like a cow. Humf put a book about dinosaurs, a fire engine and a fluffy ball into it.

Dad had to go to the supermarket to get milk. "Milk comes from cows," said Loon, looking at Humf's rucksack, but Humf couldn't see a cow anywhere.

Then Dad had to go to the bank. He had to wait in a line to see the lady behind the window. Humf and Loon didn't mind. They had things to do, too.

On the way home, Dad took Humf and Loon to the park, which was much more fun than the bank. But then Loon got upset. "My bag! My bag!" she shouted.

Loon's new handbag was gone. Humf, Loon and Dad looked all around the playground, but they couldn't see Loon's new handbag anywhere.

7

So they all went back to the supermarket
and looked around. They couldn't find
Loon's new handbag.

8

Then they went back to the bank. There was Loon's new
handbag behind the window. "It's good to have a rucksack,"
said Humf. "It stays on your back."

Let's Count!

How many pictures of Wallace can you spot?

Write your answer here.

Can you count the pictures of Loon?

Write your answer here.

How many pictures of Humf can you find?

Write your answer here.

Answers on page 65

54

Find the Giraffe

Help Wallace find his way through the maze, so he can play on the giraffe.

Match the Pair

Can you spot which two pictures of Uncle Hairy are the same?

Answers on page 65

a

b

c

d

e

Paper Aeroplanes

You will need:
- A sheet of A4 paper

1

Fold the paper in half, as shown in the picture to the right. Unfold the paper, keeping it lengthwise. Fold the top corner over to meet the centre line. Repeat, folding the other corner to meet the centre line.

2

Starting at the tip, make another fold, folding each side over so that the edges meet the centre line, as shown in the picture below.

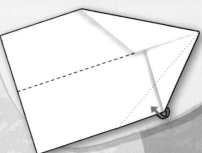

3

Fold the paper in half on the centre crease and turn it over, creating an arrow shape. Fold the wing downwards, as shown in the picture below. Repeat for the other wing.

4

Spread the two wings out and hold it so that the tip is facing away from you, as shown in the picture below. Then gently throw it to make it fly!

Stone Painting

s t e p
1

Find a smooth stone from your garden, or the park. Wash it in warm water and leave it to dry. Paint the stone all over using red paint, as shown in the picture on the right. Leave it to dry.

You will need:
- A paintbrush
- Poster paint
- PVA glue
- Smooth flat stones

t e p
2

Paint one end of the stone using black paint, as shown in the picture below. This will be the ladybug's head. Next, paint a thin black stripe down the middle of the stone. Then paint some black dots on either side.

s t e p
3

When the stone is dry, paint the stone with glue, this will act as a seal and stop the paint washing off. Leave it to dry.

s t e p
4

The painted stone can be put in the garden as an ornament, or use it as a paperweight. Find stones of all shapes and sizes and try painting different types of bugs, as shown in the pictures below!

Meet
Uncle Hairy

Humf is my nephew.

- I like playing music, especially the drums.
- My job is in an office for a company that makes dishwashers.
- I love listening to music.
- I like going to the cinema. The best movies are the funny ones
- I live in a basement flat.
- I like Chinese take-away and ice cream with biscuits in it.

Happy Drawing!

Uncle hairy is Humf's favourite uncle. They often play together and have lots of fun. Uncle Hairy likes to laugh and tell jokes.

Draw Uncle Hairy

Using the grid below, copy the picture of Uncle Hairy. Once you have finished, have fun decorating him.

Slow Down, Wallace!

One day, Humf's mum took Humf upstairs to play with Wallace. Humf rang the doorbell. Wallace ran to the door and answered. "Hello, Wallace," said Humf.

2

Wallace jumped off the sofa.
"I'm Super Tiger and I'm very fast," said Wallace.
"Peeooww! KACHOO!" Sometimes Wallace was very silly!

Humf's mum took Humf and Wallace to the park, but Wallace was still being Super Tiger. "Even Super Tiger has to hold hands to cross the road," said Humf's mum.

"Kerpow!" Wallace bumped into Humf and knocked him over! "Slow down, Wallace!" said Humf. "You have to be careful." "I'm Super Tiger!" said Wallace.

5

Loon came to play at the park, too.
"Ow!" said Loon. "Wallace! You stepped on my foot."
"It's time to stop being Super Tiger, now," said Humf's mum.

6

"Okay," said Wallace. He tried just to be Wallace for a
while. Then he forgot and turned into Super Tiger again.
"Peeowww! KACHOO!" said Wallace. BANG!

Wallace wasn't looking where he was going and he bumped his head on the swings. "Slow down, Wallace," said Humf's mum. Finally, Wallace slowed down.

Wallace even went down the slide very, very slowly! "Hurry up, Wallace!" cried Loon. Sometimes Wallace was very silly. Going slow can be fun, too.

Art Attack!

Decorate these pictures of Wallace, Humf and Loon using your best pencils and pens.

Answers

page 8

a

b

c

d

page 9

The step is blue instead of red.

page 18

a

a b c

page 19

c

a.

d.

4

3

page 54

5

page 55

b

e